# 1.
# How evolution took over

**'Darwin's theory ... is no longer a theory but a fact. No serious scientist would deny the fact that evolution has occurred, just as he would not deny the fact that the earth goes round the sun.' So spoke Sir Julian Huxley in 1959, just 100 years after Darwin first put forward his theory of evolution.**

That theory caused a storm of controversy when it appeared, and the majority of leading scientists of that day opposed it; now we are told, however, that it is no longer a theory but a fact.

In schools today children are taught as a *fact* that man has evolved from apelike creatures. In history

lessons, ape-men are presented as having had as real an existence as the Romans. The teaching of geography is affected by evolutionary views of geology.

Our whole society has in fact been influenced by the evolutionist outlook that there is no Creator, that man is continually progressing and that his

3

bad behaviour is simply the remnant of his animal past. Such views are based on the supposed 'fact' of evolution. But is it a fact? Is the theory of evolution proved?

First we must consider one particular question: how did the theory of evolution come to be so successful?

## Where did it begin?

The idea of evolution certainly did not begin with Darwin. Many scientists and philosophers believed it before his day. It arose first among the ancient Greeks; Anaximander taught that men had evolved from fish, and Empedocles asserted that animals had been derived from plants. These views, however, were not generally accepted.

## Spontaneous generation?

The reason for this was that another theory about the origin of living things became so popular that it cast evolutionary ideas into the background. This was the view known as spontaneous generation.

Spontaneous generation taught that creatures could arise suddenly from mud and slime. Aristotle and others first put this forward centuries before the birth of Christ. They believed that they could see insects and flies suddenly appearing out of mud; and if that could happen to insects, then why not to all creatures? This theory was just as unbiblical and

*William Harvey*

unscientific as that of evolution itself. Gregory pointed out in A.D. 400 that if slime was the cause of all living things, then there was no need to believe in God as Creator. His criticism was ignored, however, and spontaneous generation was believed for an incredible length of time until finally disproved by Pasteur in the 19th century.

It is astonishing that it should have been believed for so long because the great scientist William Harvey had challenged it 200 years before Pasteur. Later in the seventeenth century Redi also made a scientific investigation of spontaneous generation. His contemporaries believed that worms could arise spontaneously from decaying meat. Redi experimented by covering the meat so that the flies could not lay eggs on it – and after that worms were no longer produced.

It is no surprise that spontaneous generation was proved false; but how had it held the field for so many hundreds of years? How was it possible for a false theory to be believed so passionately and for so long against the advice of eminent scientists and contrary to scientifically controlled experiments? I believe the reasons to be exactly the same as those for which the theory of evolution is believed today. They are summed up in the opinion of the scientist Haeckel: he claimed that spontaneous generation *must* be true because otherwise it would be necessary to believe in a Creator. People believed this theory because they did not want to believe in the God of the Bible. Exactly the same is true of evolutionists today, and in some ways evolution is rather like an elaborate sophistication of that old superstition. Does it not teach that living matter suddenly 'appeared' from nonliving?

## What about fossils?

For century after century, therefore, the theory of evolution was kept from becoming popular by the dominance of an equally godless theory, that of spontaneous generation. Looking back it seems strange that fossils were not brought forward as evidence for evolution, since they are considered

*Georges Cuvier*

so important today. People certainly knew about them, for fossils were first noticed by the early Greeks. They recognized them for what they are, the petrified remains of living organisms. However, by the Middle Ages, fossils were no longer reckoned to have anything to do with living animals. People believed them to have been formed in stone by the action of the sun and stars and this superstitious view kept them from being investigated scientifically.

One of the first men to look at fossils scientifically was Ristoro d'Arezzo, a man who obviously believed in the Bible. In 1282 he suggested that all the evidence supported the Bible's account of a world-wide flood. For example, he dug up the bones of fishes as well as sea shells near a high mountain peak. About 1500, Leonardo da Vinci discovered the fossils of marine creatures while building a canal in northern Italy. The work of both these men was ignored and forgotten for hundreds of years, but it does show that the early work on fossils did not suggest the idea of evolution.

In the seventeenth century, a man called Steno put forward ideas as a result of studying rocks and fossils. He was the first to suggest that the rock strata represent layers of rock deposited on top of one another at different times in the earth's history, with the oldest layer to be found at the bottom. Steno's arguments did not lead to any general acceptance of evolutionary ideas. On the contrary, the end of the seventeenth century has been described as the 'heyday' of the

Diluvialists (those who believed that geological phenomena could be explained by the Flood). One man contributed greatly to this 'heyday'. This was John Woodward, a learned doctor, who has been sarcastically described as 'the Grand Protector of the Universal Deluge'.

Non-Christian authors have praised Woodward's work and have described him as being a very careful and exact investigator. His painstaking study of the earth's rocks and fossils certainly did not lead him to a belief in evolution. He concluded that all the evidence, far from suggesting that rock strata had been laid down at different times, spoke instead of a single world-wide flood – the Biblical deluge. The fossils, he said, were on the whole the remains of animals that had died in the Flood.

As the science of palaeontology developed and became established, it was a belief in the Flood that was often driving it. For the early palaeontologists, the study of fossils simply did not suggest the idea of evolution. Instead, the great fossil graveyards that began to come to light spoke more clearly of catastrophe. It is no exaggeration to say that virtually all the early palaeontologists were opposed to evolution, a fact acknowledged by Charles Darwin.

## Sowing the seeds of evolutionary theory

Towards the end of the eighteenth century, men began to voice ideas about evolution again. One of these was Erasmus Darwin, Charles' grandfather, who must have influenced Charles to some extent. Another was Lamarck, a man who subsequently became famous as an evolutionist. At the end of the eighteenth century he gave lectures in Paris advocating evolution, although he did not produce much evidence to support his ideas. Lamarck did not succeed in making evolution popular because once again there was opposition to the theory. This was led by Georges Cuvier, one of the greatest of the early palaeontologists, a brilliant man who enjoyed international fame and respect.

Cuvier was lecturing in Paris at

*Charles Robert Darwin*

the same time as Lamarck. Lamarck would lecture on evolution in one room to a few people, while Cuvier next door would be speaking to a packed lecture hall, opposing evolution with all his strength. In this manner, Cuvier kept evolution at bay for several more decades. He was a brilliant man, and his knowledge of fossils was astounding, yet the fossil evidence did not for one moment suggest evolution to him.

The tragedy was that, although Cuvier was so opposed to evolution, he did in fact help to sow the seeds for its later success. As the rocks and fossils began to be studied in more detail, they did not seem to Cuvier to fit into the simple flood model of the Diluvialists. He believed he could see evidence of several major catastrophes and began to teach that there had been several catastrophes of which the Flood was the most recent. In doing this, he was responding to the fossil evidence in a way that did not accord with the Bible. Cuvier had such a famous name and reputation that many followed him. Belief in

the Flood as recorded in the Bible, which had already declined since Woodward's day, was thus further undermined and this eventually helped Darwin's views to succeed.

While Cuvier was attacking evolution in the realm of palaeontology, it was beginning to make its influence felt in the realm of geology. James Hutton is called by some 'the father of geology' and in 1795 he propounded his theory of 'uniformitarianism'. This is the theory that geological processes have always been as they are now and that the earth's present form was not shaped by major catastrophes such as a world-wide flood.

One man who took up Hutton's ideas and enlarged on them was Lyell, and his work *Principles of Geology* influenced Darwin greatly. Hutton and Lyell completely abandoned the idea that a catastrophe like the Flood had ever happened. They believed that the processes going on now, such as river erosion and weathering, are quite adequate to explain the present state of the earth. They also further developed Steno's ideas, stating that the various rock strata have have been laid down over long periods of time with the oldest levels at the bottom.

## Darwin and 'The Origin of Species'

Through such men evolutionary thought developed in the centuries before Darwin, but his is the name supremely associated with the idea. Charles Darwin did not really say anything new. Most of the elements contained in his theory had already been suggested before, but they had never previously been presented so coherently or with so much supporting evidence.

What did Darwin's theory actually say? He started by assuming that the young always differ in many small ways from their parents and that these differences can be passed on to later generations. He argued that animals possessing favourable variations will increase in number, while others will tend to die out. By this process of selection, Darwin said, new species might eventually arise.

Darwin presented much evidence for his theory, but he himself said that he had been led to it through observations he had made in the Galapagos Islands off the coast of South America. Darwin noticed that the species on the Galapagos resembled those of the South American mainland but were not identical with them. For example, there seemed to be a special race of giant tortoise on each island. Darwin began to think that all these races had descended from a common type.

In the months and years following his return to England, Darwin developed his views on evolution, taking them further and suggesting that different species, rather than just races, could descend from a common ancestor. He was, however, reluctant to publish these ideas, probably because of the storm of controversy that he knew would follow publication of such a theory. After he had hesitated for twenty years, he finally published his book *The Origin of Species by Means of Natural Selection* in 1859.

The immediate effects were not very spectacular. The book sold well, but there was no widespread agreement with Darwin's views at first. Many leading scientists expressed their disagreement with the book and indeed condemned it outright as a book that could do great harm. At the beginning of the year 1860 the scientific world was almost wholly against Darwin.

What turned the tide and caused his views to become so universally accepted? A great deal of the responsibility for this can be attributed to one man, a man who had supported Darwin from the moment his book was published. This was the brilliant Thomas Henry Huxley, a scientist who took it upon himself to fight for Darwin and to promote evolution.

## Scornful bishop?

An important event took place in June 1860 at a meeting of the British Association for the Advancement of Science. As we have said, Darwin was not in the limelight and his work did not form a major part of the subjects under discussion. However, Darwin's views were raised and, because there was some controversy over them, it was decided to hold a special meeting to discuss them. This meeting took place on 30 June 1860 and it subsequently became very famous in the history of the evolution/creation debate.

The Bishop of Oxford, Samuel Wilberforce (a son of the abolitionist), undertook to address the Scientific Association and to speak against the theory of evolution. The story has been told for over a hundred years of how Huxley got much the better of him in the debate that followed and the bishop has been represented as ignorant and ill-informed. However, in recent years, this view of the matter has been challenged. It appears that there are no contemporary written accounts of what was said at that meeting. The descriptions that we do have are quoted from the memory of those who attended. In other words, all that we have is hearsay evidence often from prejudiced witnesses. From what we do know of the bishop, he was *not* ignorant and ill-informed.

*Thomas Henry Huxley versus ...*

He wrote a long critical essay on *The Origin of Species* which Darwin described as 'uncommonly clever' and which makes very good sense.

One can only assume that the story that circulated of Huxley's brilliance compared with the bishop's incompetence was put around as propaganda by those who wished to promote Darwinism. If that is so, they were certainly successful in their aims for that incident was the beginning of the landslide. Within ten years, scientific opinion throughout the world had changed in favour of evolution. This was not due solely to Huxley's eloquence, for many other factors contributed to the success of evolutionary theory. Among them were these:

1. Darwin did present a mass of new evidence which seemed to support his theory.

2. Man – then as now – was anxious to believe in anything rather than his Creator; a theory which claimed to be scientific and which could be used as an excuse for rejecting God was very attractive.

3. A large part of the Christian church immediately and tragically compromised their position and began to insist that it was quite consistent to believe both Genesis and evolution. This was both untrue and unnecessary. The two do not say the same thing and there was no reason to suggest that they should.

4. There is a further reason why the 1860s were good times for the evolutionists; I want to go into it in

some detail because I think it can teach us some valuable lessons.

We need to remember that the main thrust of Darwin's evidence concerned the different species on the Galapagos Islands. He argued convincingly that here was proof that one species of finch had evolved into another. He then suggested that in a similar way, all living organisms had evolved from a very simple organism.

Christians rose up in arms against everything that Darwin said. They seemed to think that if it was proved that one species of finch had evolved into another then Darwin's whole theory was proved. But what does the Bible actually have to say about species? Proverbs 30:5-6 says, 'Every word of God is flawless; he is a shield to those who take refuge in him. Do not add to his words or he will rebuke you and prove you a liar.' How often Christians have dishonoured the Lord by insisting on something that the Bible does not in fact say, and then being found to be liars! Does the Bible say that species cannot change? It certainly says that God created animals according to their kinds, but is a species the same thing as a kind?

### What is a kind?

The idea that species cannot change was certainly not an article of the church before the eighteenth century. It was then considered quite in accord with the Bible to believe that they could change, though not in the direction of greater complexity. It was not until the eighteenth century that the view became widespread that species cannot change, that they are 'fixed' or 'immutable'. The man responsible for promoting it was Linnaeus, who is famous as the first man to introduce systematics to biology. He maintained that species as he had defined them represented the 'kinds' of the Bible and therefore they could not change.

This view became widely accepted, insisted on and carried to absurd limits even though Linnaeus himself later amended his ideas and expressed doubts that species were completely fixed. At one time it was even taught that there were sixty species of man, each of which had

been separately created! When Darwin made his observations in the Galapagos Islands, the idea that species could not change was both a scientific and a theological dogma. When he observed evidence that suggested that they could change, Darwin said 'It is like confessing a murder.'

I would like to suggest that what the Bible describes as a 'kind' is not necessarily the same thing as a species. If Christians had not then been so insistent about the 'fixity of species' they might have noticed the sort of changes that Darwin saw in the Galapagos. They might have been able to give a better explanation for them than 'evolution', as I hope to do in succeeding chapters. They might have been able to forestall Darwin and show that while he was describing a true phenomenon, it did not necessarily prove evolution.

*... Bishop Samuel Wilberforce*

The Christians of Darwin's day, then, were meaning to be faithful when they insisted that species could not change. They did not realize that they were fighting for a man-made tradition, rather than for what the Bible actually says. Their stand did harm in two ways. First, it hindered the advance of biology, and there was therefore a reaction in favour of

Darwinism. Second, it meant that when Christians argued against evolution, they were very often arguing against the wrong thing. It was not the change in species that was the problem, but rather the idea that animals can evolve into more complex forms.

Christians may quite happily concede that one species of finch might change into another. What they do *not* believe and must fight with all their strength, is the view that this process can cause changes in the direction of greater complexity. Man has *not* evolved from the apes; mammals have *not* evolved from reptiles. God created man, fish, birds and reptiles according to their kinds in a few days and all the glory for that creation belongs to him.

We cannot avoid the fact that some blame for the triumph of evolution attaches to the Christian church. And in their day we would probably have made the same mistakes. However, it is not too late to fight back! There are signs that if we oppose evolution now, we stand a better chance of success than at any time during the last 100 years. Many scientists are now critical of evolution and the whole creation/evolution debate has opened up again. While 'creationist' might be regarded as a term of abuse in some scientific circles, it is now at least acknowledged that such a position still exists!

Christians have every reason for vigorously asserting that the scientific evidence unmistakably supports the Word of God and points to the work of a mighty Creator.

### For further reading

The facts quoted in this chapter can be verified by reference to the following:
1. Herbert *Wendt, Before the Deluge,* (Gollancz, 1968).
2. R.E.D. Clark, *Darwin, Before and After,* (Paternoster Press, 1966).
3. C.C. Gillispie, *Genesis and Geology,* (Harper and Row, 1959).
4. W. N. Edwards, *The Early History of Palaeontology,* (The British Museum, 1967).
5. R. Wrangham, 'The Bishop of Oxford: not so soapy', *New Scientist 83,* pp.450-451.

# 2.
# Just what do the fossils prove?

According to the generally accepted view, the best evidence for evolution has come from the study of fossils; a leading modern zoologist expressed this view in these words: 'The most important evidence for the theory of evolution is that obtained from the study of palaeontology. Though the study of other branches of zoology ... might lead one to suspect that animals are all interrelated, it was the discovery of various fossils and their correct placing in relative strata and age that provided the main factual basis for the modern view of evolution.'[1]

The question we must face therefore is whether the fossil record actually supports evolution, or whether it rather supports the Bible's account of special creation followed by a world-wide flood.

Until Darwin's time, the fossil record had not on the whole suggested evolution. After *The Origin of Species* became accepted, palaeontology had to be completely rethought in the light of the new ideas. By the 1880s, evolution had become scientific orthodoxy and from then on any fossil find had to be interpreted to fit in with accepted evolutionary theory. To interpret it in any other way was (and is) considered heresy.

## Fossils and the theory of evolution

It may help us to clarify the issues if we first consider what the fossil record should show according to evolutionary theory. Let us suppose that evolution has been conclusively proved by methods other than palaeontology. As we come to look at the fossils, we would expect to find the following.

An example of how fossils are found massed together. This slab of limestone is crowded with remains of ammonites **Asteroceras marstonense Spath** (large shells) and a species of **Promicroceras** (small shells).

8

*a.* At the bottom of the geological column, in the oldest rocks, very simple organisms should be found. As we progress through the various rock strata towards more recent rocks, the organisms should gradually become more and more complex.

*b.* 'Link fossils' would also be expected; these would be the remains linking groups of animals that today are widely separated – such as the fish and the amphibia, or the reptiles and the mammals. Since the process is supposed to have happened gradually, there should be many hundreds or thousands of these intermediate forms. As we reach fairly recent rocks we would expect to find clear evidence of ape-like people.

## Fossils and the biblical account

Now let us suppose that the Bible gives a true description of the early history of the earth. What then should we expect to find in the fossil record? To answer this we must consider the Bible's account of what happened in those early years.

Genesis 1 tells us that God first of all created the earth and that it was covered with water. Then he created day and night and after that he divided the waters. Water still covered the earth but now there was an expanse, or firmament, and then more water. This may mean that there was originally more water in the upper atmosphere than there is now. If so it would have had an effect on the earth's climate. On the third day, God gathered the water that remained on earth into one place and dry land appeared; in other words there may have been one ocean and one land mass. After this, God created plants, the sun and moon, animals and finally mankind. As people lived on the earth they grew more and more wicked, after the Fall, and eventually God judged them with a terrible flood. This covered the whole earth and killed all land animals and every person except those who were with Noah in the ark.

Genesis chapter 7 describes the Flood as a dreadful event, outside our present experience and hard for us to imagine. All air-breathing creatures

The evolutionary geological column

| Period | | Million years ago | |
|---|---|---|---|
| Pleistocene | Man | 2 | Age of Mammals |
| Pliocene | | 7 | |
| Miocene | Tertiary | 26 | |
| Oligocene | | 37 | |
| Eocene | Mastodon | 54 | |
| Cretaceous | Pteranodon | 136 | Age of Reptiles |
| Jurassic | Struthiomimus | 190 | |
| Triassic | Ammonite, Ruttodon | 225 | |
| Permian | Dimetrodon | 280 | Age of Amphibians |
| Carboniferous | Dragonfly, Ichthyostega | 345 | |
| Devonian | Eusthenopteron | 395 | Age of fishes |
| Silurian | Hemicylaspis | 430 | |
| Ordovician | Starfish, Brachiopods, Coral | 500 | Age of Invertebrates |
| Cambrian | Trilobite, Echinoderm | 570 | |
| Pre Cambrian | | | |

were 'wiped out'. The word means more than simply that they died. It could mean that they were totally erased from the earth. It was as though the surface of the earth experienced a 'meltdown' and the only safe place to be was in the water, where God was protecting Noah, his family and the other creatures that were in the ark. The Flood was terrifying in its destructive power and serves as a warning to mankind of the coming final judgment when the earth will be totally destroyed.

Now, if this account is true, what should the fossil record show?

*a.* As regards the nature of the earth's rocks, we would expect the Flood to have left thick layers of sediment, since this is usually the result of flooding. These vast layers would subsequently have become consolidated, forming sedimentary rock over most of the earth's surface.

*b.* It would not surprise us if the rocks contained evidence of catastrophic death. This could possibly result from the year of the Flood itself, although the devastation caused may have been too great to leave fossils. However, even if that was the case, as the earth readjusted after such a major catastrophe, the rocks could be expected to display periods of instability involving further violent death.

Now we must turn from what we might, on each view, *expect* to find and look instead at what the fossil record actually shows. Does it support evolution, or does it rather show those features implied by the Bible? We may review the evidence under six aspects.

## 1. Gradual development

Does the fossil record show evidence of a gradual development through the rocks from simple to complex organisms?

This is what we would expect to find if evolution were true. In fact, fossils representing many different kinds of animals appear suddenly in great numbers at a certain level in the earth's rocks known as the Cambrian. Below this level, in rocks referred to as 'Precambrian' hardly any fossils are found at all. Those that have been found are usually microscopic, single-celled, soft-bodied creatures such as bacteria and algae. Some fossils of a few groups of multicellular soft-bodied creatures have been found in rocks classed as 'late Precambrian', such as at Ediacara in South Australia. However, some evolutionist authorities do not believe that these are the direct ancestors of the Cambrian groups[2]. They seem to be different types of creatures that are now extinct, rather than types that could conceivably have evolved into more modern forms.

The 'Cambrian explosion', as it is known, is very embarrassing to the evolutionist. There is no gradual progression from very simple organisms to complex ones in the Cambrian rocks; rather, fossils suddenly appear representing nearly every group of organisms alive today. It is significant, moreover, that these

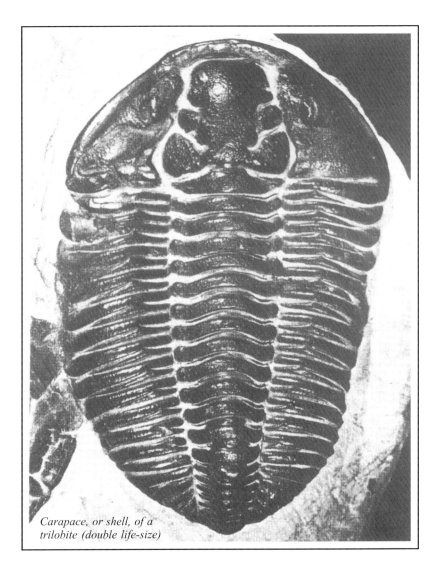

*Carapace, or shell, of a trilobite (double life-size)*

Cambrian fossils are not the simplest, least complex representatives of these groups. For example, there are vast numbers of trilobites, creatures which are now extinct but belong to the same group as the crayfish or lobster. Trilobites up to forty-five centimetres long have been found and their structure is most complex.

Fossils found in Cambrian rocks reveal a collection of complex, fully-formed, diverse invertebrates. The famous Burgess Shale fossils include representatives of about ten extinct major groups that we know nothing of today. It is as though the Cambrian, far from displaying a simple, 'half-evolved' world, reveals just the opposite, a time in the past when living things were even more diverse than they are today.

Another point to note about the Cambrian rocks is that they do not contain many fossils of the simplest organisms. For example, the Protozoa are virtually absent from the Cambrian, although a little higher in the rocks many are to be seen. Evolution teaches that all the more complex animals have evolved from the Protozoa; yet the Protozoa are virtually absent from the oldest rocks while the more complex creatures are to be found there in hundreds!

The evidence of the fossil record does not support the theory of a gradual development from very tiny organisms to complex ones; rather many complex forms appear suddenly in the rocks. This is just what we would expect from the Bible's account.

In recent years, a split has appeared in the evolutionist camp. Some evolutionists are no longer arguing for 'gradual development', for the very reasons that have been described. Instead they put forward the idea of 'punctuated equilibria', which says that evolution has happened in short, sharp jerks, followed by stable periods during which very little change has occurred. It is important to realise that this theory has been put forward as an attempt to explain the *lack* of evidence in the rocks for gradual evolution rather than because there is positive evidence for it. Those who hold to the idea of 'punctuated equilibria' also find it very hard to explain *how* these sudden bursts of rapid evolution could possibly happen. The debate between old-fashioned 'gradualist' Darwinians, such as Richard Dawkins, and palaeontologists such as Stephen Jay Gould, who know that the rocks tell a different story has been bitter and protracted and is ongoing. The difference between the two groups is profound and reveals that evolution is not the straightforward, well-established theory that it is so often made out to be but rather that it is a basic view of origins adhered to despite the evidence.

## 2. Worldwide flood?

Is there any evidence in the fossil record of major catastrophe, such as could be linked with a worldwide devastating flood?

Yes, there is, and that evidence can be summarised as follows. In the earth's rocks are to be found millions upon millions of fossilised animal remains, often grouped together in what appear to be huge 'graveyards'. There are also to be found unimaginably vast deposits of coal and oil, both of which are the remains of living organisms. Evolutionists have great difficulty explaining these things, for evolutionary theory rests largely on the concept of uniformitariansism. This is the view that geological processes have always been as they are now, and that the earth's present form was not shaped by major catastrophes – but there are no processes going on today which could produce such effects as these. Such evidence is consistent with the idea of a flood which covered the whole earth. Let us now consider the distribution of these fossils in detail.

### A. *Fossil graveyards*

All over the world, fossil bones are found remaining after the soft parts of the animal have decayed. Now creatures only become fossilised in this way if they are buried immediately. If they remain on the surface of the ground, or float in water, they will decay quickly or be eaten by other animals. Once they are buried in suitable sediment, however, decay takes place very slowly, leaving either the bones themselves or impressions of where the bones have been.

It is generally agreed that the best and most likely way for a fossil to be produced is by the sudden burial of the creature in sediment at, or soon after, death. Such a process is not happening on earth today to anything like the extent needed to produce the vast number of fossils that exist.

For example, a fish is an unlikely candidate today for becoming a fossil. Ordinarily, when a fish dies it is eaten by other fish within a matter of hours. Fossil fish are nevertheless often found in sedimentary rock. Entire shoals of fossilised fish have been found covering large areas and numbering thousands of millions. They are often found in a state of agony with no mark of a scavenger's attack.

Dinosaur fossils are also found in positions that suggest sudden violent death. An evolutionist wrote, 'Many entire skeletons of duckbilled dinosaurs have been excavated in ... a swimming position with the head thrown back as if in death throes.'[3] Evolutionists have had to develop elaborate theories to explain why these animals which are not aquatic, should have died violently in water. On the basis of the Bible's account, the answer is not difficult.

Another example of a fossil graveyard is the Cumberland Bone Cave in the American state of Maryland. In that cave the remains of dozens of species of mammals have been found together with reptiles and birds from different types of climates and habitats. Fossil hippopotamus bones are so plentiful in Sicily that they have been mined as a source of charcoal.

We could go on multiplying instances of such fossil graveyards, but there is no space. Nowhere in the world have such graveyards been found of animals who have recently died and who are awaiting fossilisation. Uniformitarianism can neither explain why so many thousands of animals died violently at the same time, nor why, having died, they were buried so rapidly in sediment. Catastrophes like the biblical Flood can.

### B. *Vast coal and oil beds*

Both coal and oil are the remains of living organisms. Coal is the remains of plants that have been altered by the effects of pressure and temperature. It is found throughout the geological column and in all parts of the world, even in Antarctica. These coal measures speak of the former existence of almost unimaginably massive accumulations of buried plants.

Uniformitarianism tries to explain the existence of coal by the ordinary death and decay of trees. It is suggested that the first stage is a peat bog which gradually turns to coal through the effect of pressure above it. However, there is no known bog or marsh containing enough peat to make a large coal seam.

*Baby woolly mammoth, dug out of frozen ground in Alasks and now preserved in a refrigerated case.*

In fact, an objective look at the coal beds strongly suggests that the plant accumulations have been washed into place by water. Many coalfields contain great numbers of coal-bearing strata interbedded with strata of other materials. These intervening strata are always said to have been water-deposited. Why then should not the coal seams have been waterborne and deposited in the same way? Joachim Scheven has put forward a creationist view of coal formation involving floating forests of a type unknown today.[4]

Uniformitarians often claim that coal and oil formation are processes that would require millions of years. However, oil has been produced in the laboratory from organic material in as little as twenty minutes. Similarly, coal has been formed from woody material in a very short time.

### C. *Polystrate fossils*

Large fossils (of animals and plants, especially tree trunks) can be found which extend through several strata often six metres or more in thickness. These fossils must have been buried quickly because their top parts are just as well preserved as those lower down. Vast amounts of sediment must thus have been deposited in a very short time. The existence of these fossils is impossible to explain if one assumes, as evolutionists do, that the different strata were laid down at different times over millions of years.

Uniformitarianism, then, cannot explain the existence of fossils in such vast numbers; catastrophes like a worldwide flood can.

### D. *Frozen animals of Siberia*

Along the coastline of Northern Siberia and into Alaska are buried the remains of about five million mammoths. On one island in this area the soil consists of sand, ice and such a quantity of mammoth bones that they seem to be the chief substance of the island. In some places the mammoths are entombed in ice; in others they are frozen into sedimentary strata. The refrigeration has been so effective that mammoth carcasses have been thawed to feed dogs.

*Coal deposits are to be found throughout the world, as shown by these horizontal coal seams in the Theron Mountains of eastern Antarctia. (This also shows that the South Pole once had a temperate climate).*

The mammoths died so quickly that in one or two cases food is preserved undigested in their stomachs and in their mouths. Grasses, bluebells, buttercups, sedges and wild beans have been found in their mouths. A few of the mammoths have been preserved whole, but most are torn to pieces. Sheep, camels, rhinos, bison, horses, tigers, oxen, lions and numerous other animals have also been found embedded in Siberian ice. All in all, the picture is one of catastrophic death involving millions of animals. No process going on *any-where* today is comparable to that which entombed and preserved all those creatures.

With such vast numbers of fossils at their disposal, the evolutionists might be expected to have amassed convincing proof of their theory. In particular, we should expect them to be able to point to link fossils showing intermediate kinds of animals linking the major groups such as the invertebrates and amongst the vertebrates – the fish, amphibia, reptiles, mammals and birds.

*Polystrate tree trunks near Saint-Etienne, France.*

### 3. Fossil links?

Do fossil links exist?

In his book on evolution published in 1967[5] A. Brouwer makes the following statement: 'One of the most surprising negative results of palaeontological research in the last century is that ... transitional forms seem to be inordinately scarce.' The writer says that in Darwin's time there might have been some excuse for this, but with the enormous number of fossil species which have been discovered since then, 'other causes must be found for the almost complete absence of transitional forms.' He thus openly admits that, for the most part, link fossils just do not exist.

Over the years, however, one or two fossils have been hailed as perfect 'missing links' and we need to look at these in more detail. In passing, it is important to stress that these claims only concern a small minority of *fossils*, not large numbers of species.

Perhaps the most famous link fossil is *Archaeopteryx,* the so-called intermediate form between the reptiles and the birds. Seven fossils of *Archaeopteryx* have been discovered, each at the same site in Germany. Although the skeleton is claimed to be in many respects reptilian, the creature possessed beautiful, fully developed feathers.

Now, it is really quite difficult to distinguish between a reptile and a bird on the basis of the skeleton. Many allegedly reptilian features of the skeleton *of Archaeopteryx* can in fact be seen in one group of birds or another. For example, the breastbone of *Archaeopteryx* is flat and this is said to be a reptilian feature; yet the entire order of birds that includes the ostriches and emus has this kind of breastbone. (Recent experts claim that the structure which was originally thought to be a breastbone is actually composed of vertebrae.) The creature has claws on its wings and this is claimed as a reptilian feature; but so have the young of a few birds today, including the ostrich.

There has been much argument and debate amongst evolutionists about the *Archaeopteryx* skeleton, but suppose for a moment that it is definitely reptilian, as some of them claim. What, then, do we make of the fact that it has such perfectly formed feathers? A feather has an extremely complex and intricate design. Evolutionists suggest that the first feather was just a frayed reptilian

*Archaeopteryx: the feathers of the wings and tail are visible at the top and bottom of the block.*

scale, but the feathers of *Archaeopteryx* are nothing like frayed scales. They are fully developed, complex feathers. If *Archaeopteryx* has a fully reptilian skeleton, then it has certainly got feathers that are fully birdlike.

There is no suggestion here of something at the half-way stage between a reptilian scale and the bird feather, which is what such an intermediate creature would be expected to possess. Nowhere does the fossil record have any sign of such a link between a scale and a feather. Indeed, many scientists believe that the seven *Archaeopteryx* fossils are those of a true bird. The hoatzin, a living species of bird alive today in the Amazon valley, is similar to *Archaeopteryx* in many important aspects.

Apart from *Archaeopteryx,* few fossils even suggest a convincing link between animals of different types. In saying this, I have not forgotten the elaborate claims that are made for the existence of 'ape-men'; the question is whether the fossil evidence supports these claims. The total evidence amounts only to a few handfuls of bones and teeth. Even if these were in perfect condition, which they are not, it is doubtful that they could tell us very much.

### Ape-man?

Professor G. von Koenigswald, an ardent supporter of the ape-man theory, wrote these words in his *Meeting Prehistoric Man:* 'Working from the skeleton alone, it is not so easy to

13

define a man in comparison with anthropoid ape. Actually, the anthropoid's skeleton differs only quantitatively from our own. The number of cranial bones and teeth is the same; the difference in the structure of hands and feet is one of degree only. It is worth noting that the mountain gorilla's foot has proved to be remarkably similar to man's ... The only distinguishing character left, therefore, is the size of the brain.'

Even that last statement is questionable, as the size of man's brain is known to be extremely variable. However, let us for the moment assume what is generally claimed – that an ape's brain is rarely larger than 600 c.c. while man's varies from 1000 c.c. - 2000 c.c. This immediately reveals the so-called Southern ape-man of South Africa as an ape, since one skull (and few of them are in a state fit to be measured) measures 482 c.c.; that is, no larger than a chimpanzee! By the same token, Neanderthal man must be regarded as superhuman, since his brain capacity on average is appreciably larger than the average value for modern man. For this and other reasons it is nowadays admitted that Neanderthal man was fully human.

Peking man is also seen to be fully human, since measurements given to the skulls found in China ranged as high as 1,300 c.c. This is also what we would expect from the evidence found at the same site of some kind of industry involving large-scale burning.

The 'ape-man' story, which we do not have time to examine in detail, is based far more on speculation and deceit than on fact, as the following example of Java man illustrates.

The original evidence on which Java man became accepted as an ape-man amounted to nothing more than one leg bone, three teeth and part of a skull. The leg bone appeared human, while the skull resembled that of an ape. However, these two fossils were found 14 metres (45 feet) apart at a level in the rock which also contained true human skulls. This latter fact was suppressed for many years. Dubois, the man who discovered these fossils, announced at the end of his life that they were not the remains of an ape-man at all, but

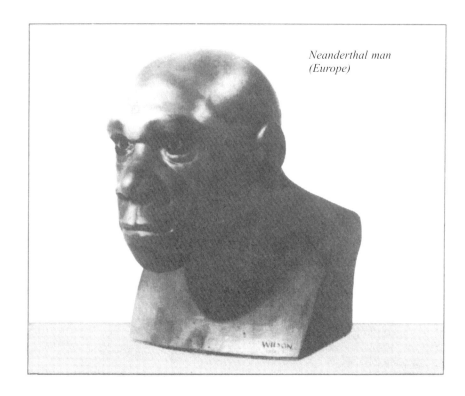

*Neanderthal man (Europe)*

rather that the skull belonged to a giant gibbon.

The evolutionist world refused to accept what he said and Java man, on the basis of this ludicrously small amount of evidence became incorporated in school textbooks as a creature who had definitely lived.

A more modern example of the same kind of 'wishful thinking' concerns some footprints found by Mary Leakey at Laetoli in East Africa. These are described in the *National Geographic,* April 1979, as being 'tracks left by hominids that walked upright at least 3.6 million years ago'. The tracks were found along with those of elephants, guinea fowl, giraffes, hares and ostriches. In this article, Mary Leakey makes some very revealing statements. On page 446 she said, 'We have found hominid footprints that are remarkably similar to those of modern man,' and on page 453, 'The form of his foot was exactly the same as ours.' In other words, she had found human footprints, exactly the same as could be made today, except that they were smaller than would be average today. As an evolutionist, she interpreted these as belonging to a 'hominid'. A creationist could equally well interpret them as belonging to an ordinary human.

Creationists who have studied the supposed 'ape-man' evidence in detail consider that the bones that have been found all belong either to humans or to extinct varieties of ape. *Bones of Contention* by Marvin Lubenow is a book which deals comprehensively with the fossil evidence, as does *Is Man Descended from Adam?* by Reinhard Junker.

## 4. Giantism

Amongst the fossils, giant forms have been discovered of almost every kind of creature alive today. Amongst the reptiles there were those enormous dinosaurs, as well as giant turtles. Mammals were often twice the size of their current counterparts. For example, giant forms of all the following mammals have been found: bears, camels, panthers, pigs, rhinos, elephants, tigers and wolves. Giant fossil birds have been found, as have insects – for example, dragonflies with 50-75 cm. wingspans.

Basic to the theory of evolution is the idea that as an animal evolves to a more complex form, it also increases in size. The very existence of these giant fossils is therefore an embarrassment to the evolutionist, although it endorses the biblical account. The subject is usually ignored by them as far as is possible.

## 5. The problem of extinction

Why did animals such as the dinosaurs become extinct? It is as though they had suddenly been wiped out completely. This applies not only to the dinosaurs but to several other groups of animals as well – for example the trilobites. Over and over again, evolutionists have to admit themselves baffled by the fact that complex, well-established groups of animals suddenly disappear from the fossil record. On the basis of Scripture, however, it is not hard to imagine how they might have been wiped out. It could have been as a result of catastrophe linked to the Flood. It is interesting that these days evolutionists themselves propose catastrophic explanations for the extinction of the dinosaurs.

## 6. The geological column

Many scientists, both creationist and evolutionist, would agree that there is a distinct order to the geologic strata, with characteristic fossils occupying the different layers. It is important to remember that the 'geological' column was worked out in the early 1800s, before Darwin published *The Origin of Species,* by men who almost universally believed in creation. Darwin lists the most eminent palaeontologists of his day and says that they 'have unanimously, often vehemently, maintained the immutability of species.'[6] From this we can see not only that it is not necessary to interpret the geological column in an evolutionary way, but also that this is not the interpretation that naturally presents itself.

In fact, the column presents a number of problems to those who wish it to support evolutionary theory. Firstly, contrary to popular belief, all the levels can rarely, if ever, be found occurring together; there are usually only two or three of these levels (or periods) that have actually been examined at any one place. Secondly, the rock layers are not always to be found in the 'right' order. In some cases, 'older' rock is on top of 'younger'. For example, the Matterhorn is composed of 'older' rock than the rock on which it rests. Some creationists believe that this sort of evidence shows the column to be more imaginary than real. Others would agree with the evolutionists that the phenomenon of 'over-thrusting' does occur as an explanation of the wrong-order sequences. However, they would point out that if huge portions of rock have really been pushed up over other layers, tremendous forces must have been involved. These forces could have been associated with a catastrophe such as the Flood and if that is the case, the scenario is an horrific one with mountains rising up and rocks crashing down. This picture would fit with the terrible judgment that the Bible describes the Flood to have been. This is an area where creationists have begun to do original research and thinking, although much more is needed.

The final point about the rocks is that three quarters of the earth's continental surface is composed of sedimentary rock, that is, rock laid down in water. The remaining quarter is largely composed of rock laid down by igneous activity. (Igneous rocks are rocks that have solidified from a molten state. This may either happen underground, or as a result of lava flowing from volcanoes.) The existence of so much sedimentary rock, occurring even on top of mountains, is consistent with the idea that the earth was once completely covered by water.

We began this chapter by listing what the fossils would be expected to show if evolution were true and *then* if the Bible were true. Without exception all the six aspects of the fossil record support the bible. The fossil record may be summarised:

*These two full-grown horses (Clydesdale and miniature) illustrate the extreme variations in size which are possible within one species. They appeared on television on 28 December 1969.*

15

1. A gradual progression of fossils through the rocks from simple to complex forms is *not* found; evolution is not proved.

2. In the vast fossil graveyards evidence is found for a catastrophe such as the Flood; the Bible is confirmed as true.

3. Reliable link fossils have not been found; evolution is not proved.

4. The giantism that has been unearthed is what we might expect from the Biblical account.; the Bible's record is confirmed.

5. The sudden extinction of animals is established as a fact and provides evidence for a major disaster like the Flood; again, this underlines the accuracy of Scripture's account.

6. The geological column does not have to be interpreted in an evolutionary and uniformitarian way. Creationist interpretations involving catastrophes are quite valid alternatives.

## References

1. G. A. Kerkut *Implications of Evolution* (Pergamon Press 1960)
2. See 'The Ediacaran Experiment', *Natural History 1984,* Vol. 93, part 2, pp. 14-23
3. Bjorn Kurten, *The Age of Dinosaurs*
4. J. Scheven. *Floating forests on firm ground*, Biblical Creation 1981, 3:9, pp. 36-43
5. *General Palaeontology*
6. *Origin of Species*, ch. 10

## For further reading

1. For general reading on fossils: Duane T. Gish, *Evolution – the Fossils Still Say No* ( Institute for Creation Research 1995)
   J. Kerby Anderson and Harold G. Coffin *Fossils in Focus* ( Zondervan Publishing House 1977)
   Luther Sutherland *Darwin's Dilemma* (Master Books 1985)
   David J. Tyler, ed., *Understanding Fossils and Earth History* (Biblical Creation Society 1984)
2. Fossil evidence of Flood catastrophe:
a. For detailed documentation see J.C. Whitcomb and H.M. Morris, *The Genesis Flood* and H. H. Howorth, *The Mammoth and the Flood* ( Sampson Low, Marston, Searle and Rivington, 1887)
b. For rapid coal and oil formation see J.C.Whitcomb, *The World that Perished* ( Baker Book House).
c. On polystrate fossils, W. Lammerts, ed., *Why Not Creation?,* (Presbyterian and Reformed 1970), p.141.
3. Link Fossils: Gerald Duffet, *Archeopteryx Lithographica Reconsidered,* (Biblical Creation Society,1983)
   Marvin L Lubenow *Bones of Contention* (Baker Book House 1992)
   Reinhard Junker, *Is Man Descended from Adam?* (Biblical Creation Society 2000)

*The coelacanth: this type of fish was said by evolutionists to have died out 70 million years ago. Recently, however, it was discovered alive, looking exactly like its fossil ancestor.*

# 3.
# Genetics and God's natural selection

It was a summer's day in a monastery garden in Czechoslovakia over 100 years ago. Most of the monks saw nothing special about the pea plants growing there. To one of them, however, they were of great interest because he was performing scientific experiments with them.

What particularly fascinated Gregor Mendel was the way in which the plants handed on their characteristics to the next generation. 'What would happen,' he thought, 'if I crossed a white-flowered plant with a red-flowered? Would the next generation have red flowers or white? What if I crossed a tall plant with a short one? What height would the offspring be?'

As Mendel performed these experiments and carefully analysed the results, he realized that he had discovered some fundamental laws concerning inheritance. Greatly excited, he published his findings in a scientific journal - but the scientific world ignored Mendel's work completely. Discouraged, he abandoned his research. When he died in 1884, Mendel had no idea that twenty years later he would have become world-famous as the founder of a new science. Mendel's work is now regarded as the beginning of the science of genetics, the study of inheritance.

In the preceding chapters we have looked at the rise of evolutionary theory and the evidence of the fossil record. Now we must consider whether – as is generally claimed – the findings of genetics support the idea of evolution.

Mendel published his findings in the late 1860s at just the time when Darwin's theory was becoming immensely popular. Mendel published in a reputable journal and his paper was widely circulated and certainly known about. Yet it was not until 1900, sixteen years after Mendel's death, that the work was rediscovered and its importance realized.

Why were such vital discoveries ignored? The answer almost certainly is that they conflicted with Darwin's theory of evolution. This is seldom admitted today, yet it is still true that what Mendel discovered disproved one of Darwin's most important assumptions. This is demonstrated by the fact that after Mendel's work was rediscovered, Darwinian evolution suffered a temporary eclipse. After a while, evolutionary thinking re-emerged in a slightly different form which was said to be quite consistent with Mendel's genetics. As we shall see, however, the two are not consistent and both cannot be true.

## Mendel's experiment

What did Mendel discover that spoke against Darwin's theory of evolution? This can best be answered by considering what he actually did. Mendel crossed various races of edible peas. When a red-flowered plant was

*Gregor Mendel*

crossed with a white-flowered, the offspring were found to be red-flowered. Mendel then crossed these red offspring with each other and found that they produced offspring of their own in the ratio of 3 reds: 1 white.

We can best understand this by considering the genes involved in these crosses. A gene can be considered as a unit which determines a particular characteristic, in this case flower colour. It can exist in one of two forms, one giving rise to red flowers and the other to white. The offspring of the original cross of red-flowered plants with white were all red-flowered, although they did in fact possess both a gene for red flowers and a gene for white.

Mendel concluded that the red gene must be dominant to the white, so that any plant that possessed them both would be red. When these red plants were bred with each other, it was possible for two white genes to come together and so give offspring that were white. The chance that the offspring would receive at least one red gene is 3:1, as the diagram shows.

*New genes or old?*

Mendel found that when he interbred the red-flowered plants obtained as the offspring of his original cross, he got white flowers produced as well as red. Darwin's theory rested on the assumption that in such a case as this the white characteristic was a new character acquired by the young plants which their parents had not possessed. After all, a race has got to acquire new characteristics if it is ever going to evolve.

Mendel showed that the characteristic had not been acquired. It had been present all the time in the parents' generation, though masked by a more dominant gene. If one applies statistics to Mendel's ideas one can show quite easily that the genes in the new generation exist in exactly the same frequency as they did in the parents' generation. It might be possible to lose some genes by killing off those individuals that possessed them but it would never be possible to acquire new ones.

It was not surprising that Darwin's theory began to flounder when these facts came to light. It was saved from total eclipse by the emergence of a theory which said that genes could sometimes change to completely new forms. This radical change in the gene is known as a mutation.

This is the form in which Darwin's theory is believed today. It is assumed that mutations can change the gene to a new form. The process of natural selection is said to operate by selecting out those new genes which are favourable to the organism and discarding others.

Until recently, evolutionists claimed that the classic example of this was the case of the peppered moth. In the 1860's this moth was pale in colour, although a rare dark

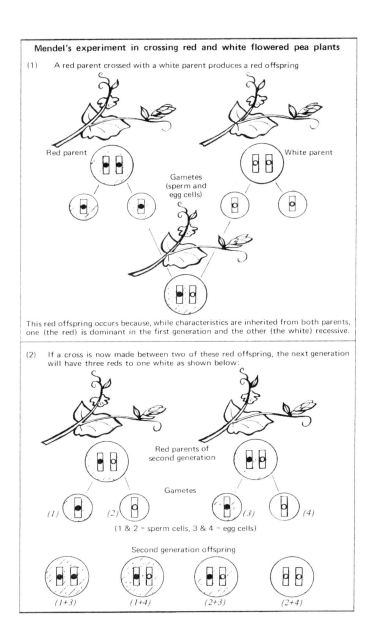

**Mendel's experiment in crossing red and white flowered pea plants**

(1) A red parent crossed with a white parent produces a red offspring

Red parent

White parent

Gametes (sperm and egg cells)

This red offspring occurs because, while characteristics are inherited from both parents, one (the red) is dominant in the first generation and the other (the white) recessive.

(2) If a cross is now made between two of these red offspring, the next generation will have three reds to one white as shown below:

Red parents of second generation

Gametes

*(1)* *(2)* *(3)* *(4)*

(1 & 2 = sperm cells, 3 & 4 = egg cells)

Second generation offspring

*(1+3)* *(1+4)* *(2+3)* *(2+4)*

form was known to exist. During the next 100 years, the dark form became more and more common until eventually the light form was rare. The reason for the change was said to be that the dark form had been at a disadvantage originally, as it showed up clearly against the lichen on the bark of trees and was therefore easy prey for predators. The light form was not easily seen and therefore escaped from the predators. With the industrial revolution, however, the trees became blackened by soot, the lichen died and the situation was reversed. The pale form was now conspicuous to predators, while the dark form escaped. However, it is now realised that peppered moths do not rest on tree-trunks in the wild and that photographs suggesting that they do have been staged, calling into ques-

tion the whole 'peppered moth' story. Nevertheless, as a story, it does illustrate, in principle, the idea of natural selection. New genes will be selected out if they confer an advantage on the organism, and it is supposed that new genes can arise by mutation.

**Mutation**

The modern theory of evolution thus stands or falls on this question of mutation. If mutations do not occur, it is impossible for evolution to progress. We must therefore examine the question of mutations and see if they actually occur as evolutionists claim.

Firstly, it is certain that mutations can and do occur. Secondly, it is just as certain that any major change in a gene is always a change for the worse. This is what we would expect. Genes are complicated and wonderfully designed and any major change in them will lead to their functioning less efficiently.

This is admitted by geneticists after a century of intensive experimentation. During that time they have induced thousands of mutations in various organisms, but have not been able to come up with one convincing case of a mutation that 'added complexity'. In fact, it is now generally admitted that mutations under natural conditions are so rare, and so often harmful, that when they do occur they are not of any significance to the genetics of a population of creatures. Any individuals who do receive the mutations will tend to die out and so the genetic structure of the population as a whole will remain unaffected.

Mutations are far from being able to produce new, vigorous genes which would enable a race of organisms to evolve. They are extremely rare and detrimental events which do not alter the genetic structure of the race as a whole – except in some cases to weaken it. This even applies to so-called favourable mutations such as the sickle cell anaemia trait and the drug-resistance of bacteria, but space will not allow discussion of these. But even if mutations were to occur in the way that evolutionists claim, evolution would still be impossible.

*A personal testimony*

A personal testimony may explain what I mean by that last statement. It concerns how I reached my present views on evolution, for my rejection of evolution on scientific grounds began over this question of mutation theory. I was first taught evolution in detail at school where I studied it during an A-level zoology course. I was taught it as though it were a fact and that it had occurred by the processes of mutation and natural selection.

I then went to the University of Sussex where for three years I studied biology, taught from an evolutionary point of view. I was a Christian all this time; at first I believed that one could believe both the Bible and

evolution, but as my time at Sussex went on I became increasingly unhappy about this. I realized that both could not be true. As a Christian I believed the Bible to be true; at the same time, I had been taught that evolution was a proved fact. This dilemma continued until well into my final year.

The turning-point came one day at a seminar when we were discussing the evolution of the vertebrate eye. The eye is an extremely complex organ. It has the complicated system whereby light is directed to the back of the eye on to cells which are sensitive to it; it also has that even more intricate arrangement whereby the information then travels to the visual part of the brain so that we actually see something.

We began at that seminar to discuss how this marvellous organ might have evolved. For an hour we argued round and round in circles. Its evolution was clearly impossible. All the specialized and complex cells that make up our eyes are supposed to have evolved because of advantageous mutations in some more simple cells that were there before. But what use is a hole in the front of the eye to allow light to pass through, if there are no cells at the back of the eye to receive the light? What use is a lens forming an image if there is no nervous system to interpret that image? How could a visual nervous system have evolved before there was an eye to give it information?

We discussed the problem from every possible angle, but in the end had to admit that we had no idea how this might have happened. I then said

that since we had found it impossible to describe how the eye could have evolved, the honest and scientific thing was to admit the possibility that it had not evolved. My words were followed by a shocked silence. The lecturer leading the seminar then said that he refused to enter into any controversy, while others in the group began to mock me for believing in God. I had not mentioned God! I had simply been trying to view the problem in an objective and scientific way.

It then became clear to me that the theory of evolution is unscientific and that mutation theory is hopelessly inadequate. It could not possibly account for the development of even the simplest organism, much less such wonders as the vertebrate eye.

*Other evidence*

I am not alone in believing that even if beneficial mutations could occur, they would not be adequate to explain evolution. A well-known biologist, Sir Alistair Hardy, has also pointed this out. In his book *The Living Stream* he reminds us of one of the most basic ideas of evolution – that the same organ in different animals is said to have evolved from the same structure in a single common ancestor.

Take, for example, the flipper of a seal, the arm of a man and the wing of a bird. Although these differ in form and function, they all have the same basic arrangements of bones. It is therefore assumed that all these creatures have evolved from some primitive vertebrate which itself had this basic arrangement of bones. Structures like this which are believed

*Light and dark peppered moths (of Birmingham). The two pictures show the visibility factor on light and dark backgrounds. These pictures have now been shown to have been staged, as the moth does not naturally rest on tree trunks.*

to have evolved from one single common ancestor are known as homologous structures.

Another example of a homologous organ may be seen in the fly. There are many different types of fruit fly and some have eyes that are quite different in appearance. Although they look different, the evolutionist assumes that they have all evolved from some earlier type of eye. They are therefore homologous. Evolutionary theory says that all the homologous organs now in existence have evolved through mutation in the genes controlling the original organ. In other words, the genes producing the homologous organs now are the same genes that produced the ancestral organ; it is just that the structure of the genes has changed.

The great problem for evolutionists is this: in many cases it can be shown that what they call homologous organs are produced by the action of quite different genes. For example, there are two races of fruit fly with eyes that must be regarded by evolutionists as homologous, yet the eyes in the two cases are definitely produced by different genes.

This is no isolated case. Over the years many examples of this have come to light. It cannot be denied that the concept of homology in terms of similar genes handed on from a common ancestor has broken down. This even applies to the famous example of the vertebrate forelimb. Consider the genes that governed the development of the forelimb of that original ancestral vertebrate. You can change those genes by mutation a million times if you want to! It will never cause the forelimb to change into a seal's flipper or a man's arm, since these are controlled by different genes!

For the past century scientists have claimed that the study of genetics supports evolution theory. So far, we have looked at objections to the claim. We saw first that Mendel's original experiment showed that new characteristics are not acquired by a population, but rather handed on directly from parent to child in the form of genes. There is thus no change from generation to generation by which evolution could occur. We next saw

that the mutation theory advanced by evolutionists to overcome this objection is itself inadequate to explain evolution. In other words, genetics does not support evolutionary theory.

## Natural selection

Much more must be said, however, concerning the truth about genetics. Far from supporting evolutionary theory, the research of the past century points to only one conclusion: evolution cannot have happened and the Bible is vindicated. Let us consider a theoretical case of what the evolutionists call natural selection and then follow it through to its logical conclusion.

Imagine a population of sea birds which can exist in one of several different colours. As the population increases, some birds colonize a neighbouring island which is dark in colour. The white and pale grey birds on this island are easily seen by predators and destroyed. The dark-coloured birds cannot be seen and so survive. Gradually a race of dark birds develops as all the light ones die out.

A similar process occurs on another nearby island, except that this time the island is light-coloured so that the race of birds that develops is light. Thus by natural selection two races of birds have developed from the original population. Eventually these might be considered new species.

*Depletion of the gene pool*

Evolutionists say that it is by this kind of process that evolution occurs. But what has happened from the genetic point of view? In the original population, genes existed for black, dark-grey, light-grey and white colour. On the black island this became depleted to black and dark-grey genes only, since the light-grey and white genes had been lost through the death of the light-coloured birds.

Natural selection thus made the gene pool poorer. There are fewer forms of the gene present, not more, as the theory of evolution would require (for unless a population gains new genes it could never become more complex).

Since the new population of dark birds is genetically poorer it is more prone to extinction. A slight change in the environment, such as the island becoming lighter, would enable the race to be wiped out by predators.

If such a process has been happening on a large scale we would expect to find that many species have become extinct and this is exactly what history demonstrates. In other words, natural selection tends towards genetic death and not to the development of more complex species.

We have seen that the process of natural selection leads to new varieties of creatures which are much poorer in genes than the earlier population from which they developed. From the evolutionist's point of view, this means that the amoeba-like creatures from which we have all evolved must have had an infinitely richer and more varied gene pool than our own!

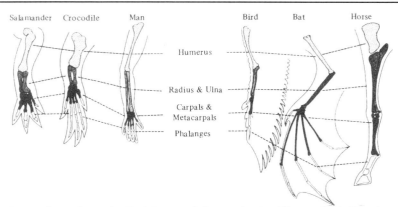

*Comparison of anterior limb bones of six vertebrates. Those who believe in evolution interpret similarities of limb bones in vertebrates to suggest common ancestry. Creationists simply affirm that the Creator chose to use a common pattern. Both interpret the evidence according to previous beliefs.*

**How natural selection works**

1) Gene pool consisting of four factors (or alleles) controlling colour

3) The dark island exposes the light-coloured birds to predators. These birds are thus in time exterminated – and the gene pool is depleted. Eventually only dark birds remain on the dark island.

2) As the seabirds increase with breeding, some birds move to colonise the dark island

4) When the light island is colonised, the dark birds are gradually exterminated – and once more the gene pool is depleted. Only light birds remain on the light island.

Eventually birds on the light and dark islands come to be regarded as two separate species.

This is clearly ridiculous. From a truly scientific point of view, groups of animals must once have existed possessing a rich variety in their characteristics from which have developed the more specialized types that we have today. I believe that this is what the Bible is speaking of when it says that God created animals 'according to their kinds'.

We see in this process of natural selection not the means by which evolution has progressed but rather the great wisdom and mercy of God. Remember that the climate that we have on earth now is not the same as that which prevailed when the earth was first created. The world-wide Flood in the time of Noah brought about immense changes. God in his great wisdom had created men and most animals with sufficient genetic adaptability for them to survive these great changes. Some, like the dinosaurs, were not able to adapt and therefore died out. We have today such creatures as tropical fish and polar animals that are confined to narrow climatic regions. Natural selection must have allowed these to survive from the original populations that God created.

The process of natural selection thus operates on factors already present in the population. For example, the dark form of the peppered moth already existed before natural selection caused it to become the most common form of the moth. God created us with a far greater potential than was needed at first. Adam must have possessed the genetic potential sufficient for all the present races of mankind.

## Additional Note

In recent years, there has been a very interesting development in the creation versus evolution debate, particularly in the United States. This has been the emergence of the 'Intelligent Design' movement , led by Harvard-trained lawyer Phillip Johnson and involving scientists such as the biochemist Michael Behe. These highly-trained and well-respected academics are arguing persuasively that the more that is discovered in the field of molecular biology, the more impossible it is to believe that such complexity has arisen by chance. The movement holds conferences, publishes a journal, 'Origins and Design' and has produced several important books, especially Michael Behe's *Darwin's Black Box*.

A further interesting development has been the publication of the results of the Human Genome Project. Scientists have been astonished to discover that the number of human genes is much lower than had been expected. The estimated 30,000 human genes that have been identified cannot possibly account for human complexity under the simple view of 'one gene for one protein' that scientists have worked with up to now. In other words, we understand much less than we thought we did about how the genes function.

## For further reading

1. Lane P. Lester and Raymond G. Bohlin, *The Natural Limits to Biological Change* (Zondervan Publishing House 1984). A comprehensive evaluation of Darwinism, Neo-Darwinism and 'punctuated equilibrium.'
2. Michael J. Behe, *Darwin's Black Box* (The Free Press 1996)
3. Four books by Phillip Johnson, all published by IVP,
   a. *Darwin on Trial* 1993
   b. *Reason in the Balance* 1995
   c. *Defeating Darwinism by Opening Minds*
   d. *Objections Sustained* 1998
4. Jonathan Wells, *Icons of Evolution* (Regnery 2000). A very important book, showing that most of the main lines of evidence quoted in favour of evolution are wrong and expanding on several of the issues related to genetics that have been dealt with in this chapter.

*California Redwoods, among the oldest living things – up to 4,000 years old.*

samples yield anomalously old K/Ar dates, sometimes greater than the accepted age of the earth.'[1]

Such anomalous results are not surprising, since as much as 1% of the earth's atmosphere consists of argon. Since rocks easily absorb this gas, how is one to know how much of the isotope argon-40 has come by decay from potassium and how much from the atmosphere?

In order to assess how much argon might have come from the air,

scientists look for the presence of a rare isotope of argon,$^{36}$Ar. This is present as a small proportion of the atmosphere but is not a decay product of potassium. Since the proportion of $^{36}$Ar in the air is known and assumed to have been always the same, its presence indicates the total amount of argon in the potassium that has come from the atmosphere.

There is, of course, no evidence of the proportion of $^{36}$Ar having been constant in the past. On the contrary,

it is probable that it is increasing as a result of cosmic rays bombarding the earth's outer atmosphere. Thus, if a rock contains only a small percentage of $^{36}$Ar, this does not necessarily mean that there has been little atmospheric contamination; rather, atmospheric argon may have been trapped at a time in the past when the percentage of $^{36}$Ar was lower. Alternatively, the calculations may be upset by the fact that $^{40}$Ar can be concentrated in the surface rocks

24

as a result of having risen from greater depths where the pressure was higher. This concentration would suggest a greater age for the rocks than actually was the fact.

The unreliability of the radio active dating methods is well illustrated by the fact that rock samples from twenty-two volcanic rocks in various parts of the world that are known to have been formed during the past 200 years gave ages ranging from 100 million to 10,000 million years by typical radioactive techniques!

Another important assumption underlying all radioactive dating methods is that the rate of decay has always been the same in the past. It is usually claimed that all the measurements taken over the past 100 years have shown them to be constant. However, this is not the case. A review of the literature published in 1976 showed that up until 1975 approximately 50 experiments had been reported which showed changes to the radioactive decay of different isotopes produced mainly by changing their chemical environments.[2] If it could be proved that decay rates had been significantly higher in the past, then all the published dates using radioactive methods would have to be revised downwards. This whole issue is at present being actively researched by creationist scientists.

Some of the problems that have already been discussed are well recognised by scientists working on dating methods and they have made attempts to deal with them. One such attempt is the 'isochron' method which claims to eliminate guesswork about the initial concentration of parent atoms. Several samples are taken from the piece of rock that is being investigated, the amount of parent and daughter isotope in each sample is measured and the results plotted on a graph. A sloping line is drawn through the data and the slope of the line is used to calculate the 'age' of the rock. With this method, you do not need to make assumptions about how much of the parent and daughter isotopes were there to start with. However, the method still makes relies on the other two assumptions, namely that none of the

material has been lost or added to, and that the decay rate has been constant. Also, two further unverifiable assumptions have to be made: the samples must all have initially formed at the same time and the daughter isotope must have spread evenly through all the samples when the rock was formed. In practice, the isochron method has sometimes given rise to anomalous results and there is reason to believe that isochrons are often produced when magmas from different sources are mixed.[3]

Radioisotope dating is certainly a very complex and highly technical subject. For several years, a consortium of professional scientists who are committed to creationism and who believe the earth to be young have been working together to develop the subject further. Known as the RATE group (standing for Radioisotopes and the Age of the Earth) they have just released a major book. Over the coming years, they will be continuing to research several key topics including isochrons and nuclear decay rates.

What, then, does the Bible teach to be the true age of the earth? Some Christians have believed that the genealogies listed in Genesis 5 and 11 are complete and that the creation can therefore be accurately dated at 4004 BC, i.e. 6000 years old. Others believe that Genesis 11 is not a strict chronology and that the earth might be somewhat older than this, possibly as much as 10,000 years. The majority of Christians who interpret Genesis in its natural sense would agree that there is no possibility of stretching the length of time given in the text any further than this. It is very significant that until the end of the eighteenth century Christians were virtually unanimous in the belief that the earth was about 6000 years old according to the teaching of Scripture. Those Christians who wish to interpret the Bible as teaching an old earth have to believe that God allowed almost all his people to be deceived until modern science came along to enlighten them. I consider this to be an extremely unlikely state of affairs.

Is there anything in the discoveries of science that would suggest the

earth to be as young as 10,000 years? It must be remembered that the worldwide Flood would have produced such drastic changes in the earth as to make dating any earlier than this extremely difficult. It could be argued that such a global disaster would disrupt all the 'clocks' and make dating meaningless. Nevertheless there are indications that the world is not nearly so old as evolutionists claim. Here are two examples of them.

*1. Atmospheric helium.*

Helium is continuously being formed by the disintegration of uranium or thorium in the earth's crust. However, there is not nearly enough helium in the atmosphere to correspond to the supposed age of the earth and the rate of escape of helium from the rocks. It has been calculated that the time required to reach the helium concentration of today's atmosphere would be 1.76 million years.[4] This is a maximum age because the calculation assumes there was no helium in the atmosphere to start with. Scientists try to get round this problem by assuming that helium is overcoming gravity and escaping from the atmosphere, but there is no evidence that anything of this kind is happening.

The amount of helium in the rocks is another key issue and is one of the research projects being undertaken by the RATE group.

*2. Salt in the sea*

Salt is continually being washed into the sea. It has been calculated that, even allowing for the formation of rock salt by evaporation and making the unlikely assumption that no salt was there in the first place, an absolute maximum of 200 million years would give the amount now found. Again, this is far short of the 1,000 million years required by evolution. The Christian, of course, believes that God would have created the sea with the correct content of salt needed to support the marine life he intended it to contain.

These lines of evidence suggest that the earth is very much younger than the 4,600 million years claimed by the evolutionist. The fact that the

*If the world is as old as is often claimed, why is there not more salt in the sea?*

found in sedimentary rocks and radioactive dating techniques can only be performed on igneous rocks. (Attempts have been made to date sedimentary rocks, but they are regarded by most people as highly unsatisfactory.) It is therefore necessary for suitable igneous rock to be found in association with the fossil-bearing rock.

This problem applies to the uranium methods of dating. We have already given an example of the uranium dating of rock containing fossils where the estimates ranged from 380 – 800 million years. Uranium cannot be used to date anything younger than 10 million years and is not considered useful for dating fossils.

Potassium/argon dating can in theory be used to date younger rock, but again it cannot be used to date fossils directly. The ancient '1470'

dates they provide still sometimes run into millions of years should not worry the Christian; as we have shown, they all depend on assuming that processes have been constant in the past and on unprovable assumptions concerning the original state of the earth. These processes, however, have not always been constant, and the Flood was a major catastrophe during which substantial physical changes happened very rapidly. Moreover, the earth – created complete and perfect by God – would after six days of existence already have achieved the form that the evolutionist imagines it would have acquired very gradually.

## II. How long has life existed on earth?

Evolutionists claim that life has existed on earth for millions of years. The chief indicators of life in the past are fossils and archaeological remains.

How do scientists generally date fossils? In recent years, radioactive dating methods have mainly been used. It is important to realize that only in rare cases can the fossils themselves be dated. Most dating methods depend on dating the rock in which the fossils are found. However, this rock itself cannot be dated directly either, since all fossils are

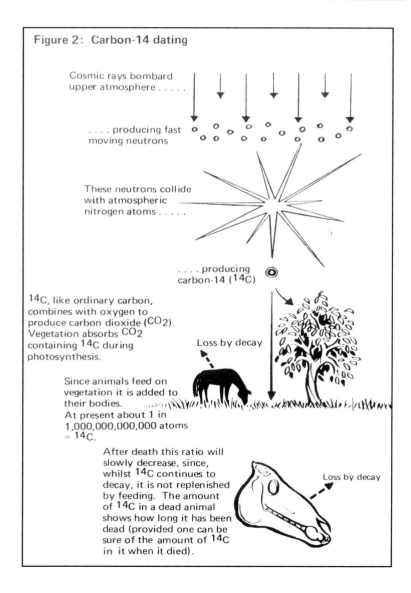

Figure 2: Carbon-14 dating

Cosmic rays bombard upper atmosphere . . . . .

. . . . producing fast moving neutrons

These neutrons collide with atmospheric nitrogen atoms . . . . .

. . . . producing carbon-14 ($^{14}C$)

$^{14}C$, like ordinary carbon, combines with oxygen to produce carbon dioxide ($CO_2$). Vegetation absorbs $CO_2$ containing $^{14}C$ during photosynthesis.

Loss by decay

Since animals feed on vegetation it is added to their bodies. At present about 1 in 1,000,000,000,000 atoms = $^{14}C$.

After death this ratio will slowly decrease, since, whilst $^{14}C$ continues to decay, it is not replenished by feeding. The amount of $^{14}C$ in a dead animal shows how long it has been dead (provided one can be sure of the amount of $^{14}C$ in it when it died).

Loss by decay

man found by Richard Leakey and assigned an age of 2.6 million years was dated by this method. The dating expert responsible, Professor E. T. Hall, reported that the first rock sample analysed 'gave the impossible date of 220 million years'. This date was rejected simply because it did not fit in with evolutionary ideas, and a second sample was analysed. This gave the more acceptable date of 2.6 million years. Subsequent tests resulted in a range of dates from 290 thousand years to 19.5 million years. This example illustrates both the unreliability of the K/Ar method and also the suspect manner in which evolutionists interpret the data.

A method of dating by radioactivity which is useful both to the palaeontologist and to the archaeologist is the carbon-14 method (named after the radioactive isotope of carbon). This can in theory be applied directly to fossils themselves, whereas all other methods depend on dating rocks in which fossils are found. The carbon-14 method was developed by Libby in the late 1940s and is described in Figure 2. However, it can only be used in dating materials up to 40,000 years old, and is mainly used for studying glacial and postglacial geology and archaeology.

The theory assumes that carbon-14 is in equilibrium in the atmosphere – that it is being broken down at the same rate at which it is being produced. However, calculations made to test this assumption suggest that carbon-14 is being produced nearly one third faster than it is disintegrating. If this is true, then none of the fossils that have been dated by this method could be more than a few thousand years old. Scientists, unwilling to accept this conclusion, have preferred to assume that carbon-14 is in equilibrium, despite the evidence to the contrary.

Thus we have seen that evolutionists have no really reliable method of dating fossils. Many Christians believe that the majority of the fossils are the remains of creatures that died in the Flood or have died in subsequent disasters. Therefore, the date of the Flood would give the maximum age of most of the fossils.

To attempt to date anything before the Flood would be an extremely dif-

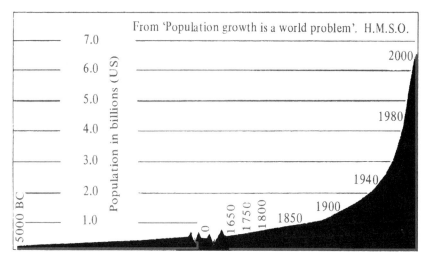

*World population grew very slowly until 1650, but then increased from 545 million to 2.5 billion in 1950. By the mid 1980s it had reached about 4.5 billion – and in the year 2000 stood at about 6 billion.*

ficult task, as we have seen, but is there any evidence that life on earth today stems from the survivors of the Flood of a few thousand years ago? There is, and the evidence can be summarized as follows.

1. There is no trustworthy, recorded history dating earlier than about 3,000 BC. Many different lines of historical evidence point back to a time about 5,000 years ago as dating the beginning of true civilization. Professor Libby learned this when he tried to verify his carbon-14 method. He said 'The first shock Dr Arnold and I had was when our advisers informed us that history extended back only to 5,000 years... You read statements in books that such and such a society or archaeological site is 20,000 years old. We learned rather abruptly these numbers, these ancient ages, are not known accurately; in fact, it is at about the time of the First Dynasty in Egypt that the first historical date of any real certainty has been established.'[5]

2. The present world population figure of 6,000 million is not consistent with the view that man has existed for millions of years. In fact it would only require about 5,000 years for this figure to be reached, as United Nations data shows.

3. If human history is really so long as evolutionists believe, why do we not have much more evidence of ancient life? Where are the graves of all the humans who are supposed to have died over hundreds of thousands

of years? And why was development so very slow up until 5000 years ago when it suddenly began to happen very quickly? Is it very likely that humans used the same stone tools for hundreds of thousands of years without making any further progress?

Having examined the questions 'How old is the Earth?' and 'How long has life existed on earth?', we have seen that science can provide no definite answer to them. The results obtained depend entirely on the method used and all the methods rely on unprovable assumptions.

We are not dealing here with accurate and straightforward measurements. When we try to measure the distant past, we must inevitably make big assumptions which are impossible to test. The enormous and quite unjustified assumption made by all the scientists we have considered has been that the conditions that prevailed at the beginning of the earth's history have continued to the present with very little change. The question we must ask these scientists is the question that God put to Job: 'Where were *you* when I laid the foundation of the earth?'

The only way for us to know the age of the earth accurately is to have it revealed to us by one who himself was present when the earth was made. Where scientists can rely only on guesswork, the Christian has a more certain source of knowledge in the Bible. Who are we to question its God-given time scale?

'Where were you when I laid the
earth's foundation?...
Who marked off its dimensions?...
Who stretched a measuring line
across it?
On what were its footings set,
Or who laid its cornerstone...?
(Job 38:4-6)

'Will the one who contends with the
Almighty correct him?
Let him who accuses God answer
him!' (Job 40:2)

## Additional notes

### 1. Second law of thermodynamics

The phenomenon of radioactive decay which we have been considering is a specialized case of a law of science which is a great embarrassment to evolutionary theory – the second law of thermodynamics. This second law is as basic to the whole of science as the first. (A 'law' here simply means a description of what regularly, universally happens in the natural realm.)

Both laws follow directly from what the Bible teaches us about the origin of the earth. The first law states that the total amount of energy in the universe is constant, that is, that energy can neither be created nor destroyed. This is what we should expect, as the Bible teaches that, after six days, God's creative activity ended. However, this law is a big problem for the 'Big Bang' theory which states that energy and matter were created out of nothing.

The second law presents problems for the theory of evolution. It states that although the total amount of energy remains constant, the amount that is available for use is constantly decreasing. Examples of this abound. To build a complicated piece of machinery (such as a car) requires a great deal of energy – it is rather unlikely that any piece of machinery would ever arise by chance! On the other hand, if your car is left to itself and never serviced, it will soon begin to rust – and finally become a heap of scrap metal.

This breaking-down process is a general law of nature. Every natural system when left to itself tends to run down, break down, become more random and less highly organized. As the years pass, for example, we get older – no one can expect to get younger and more vigorous. Or if we put a hot cup of tea in a cold place, it will cool down, not get hotter! These obvious happenings are aspects of the general 'running down' process described in the second law of thermodynamics.

Now if the second law is true, evolution is impossible. The second law shows that order cannot possibly arise by chance; the tendency is all the other way. Yet evolution teaches that incredibly complicated living organisms did arise by chance! It is time that evolutionists faced this problem. The attempts to explain it away have been pathetic. For example, it is often claimed that the second law of thermodynamics applies only to closed systems, and that because the earth constitutes an open system with energy being supplied to it from the sun, evolution could take place. However, as Duane Gish has pointed out, there are four conditions that must be met before complexity can be generated in a system. These are:

1. The system must be an open system.

2. An adequate external energy source must be available.

3. The system must possess energy conversion mechanisms.

4. A control mechanism must exist within the system for directing, maintaining and replicating these energy conversion mechanisms. Conditions 1 and 2 alone are *not* sufficient.[6]

It is time for evolutionists to admit that their theory contradicts one of the most universally verified of all the laws of science.

### 2. The age of the stars

How can the stars be only a few thousand years old? Surely they are so far away that their light has taken billions of years to reach us? I am often asked such questions, but the questioners do not realize that they are thinking in evolutionary terms. They are assuming that at a certain point in the past, the stars – as a result of one evolutionary process or another – acquired a sufficient level of energy to start emitting light rays which then began to travel across

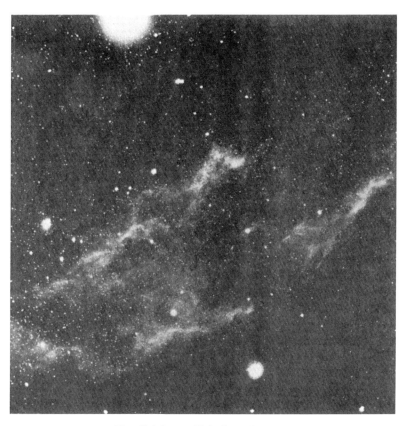

*The California Nebula in Perseus*

billions of miles of space until they eventually reached us. The Bible tells us something quite different. In Genesis 1:1 7 we are told that the sun, moon and stars were created 'to give light on the earth'. The obvious implication is that this was to happen immediately. How God achieved this is not open to scientific investigation. It was part of the miraculous creation week.

It is important to note that there is no scientific evidence against this. Scientists have never seen a star evolve. Their ideas about how stars came into being are purely speculative, although one would never realize this when reading modern books on astronomy.

This is not to deny that there are several features of the universe that creationists need to explain; for example, the existence of super-novae (stars that have exploded) at apparently great distances. Creationists have made a number of proposals to explain these phenomena. One of these is that the speed of light was greater in the past than it is now. Although this is a controversial theory, there does seem to be some evidence to support it. Recently, several leading theoretical physicists writing in the journal *Physical Review*, have suggested something similar – that is the speed of light has varied and was greater in the past.

It needs to be remembered that the vast distances quoted are not really known with certainty. This point is illustrated by the controversy over the position in the universe of the quasars. While most astronomers believe that some of these objects are as much as ten billion light years away, some have always maintained that they are in fact quite close to us. Recent evidence supporting the latter position is quoted in an article in the *New Scientist*[7] where we are told that 'The whole of quasar theory is built up from so little direct evidence... that it is possible that all these ideas are wrong.' Caution is thus needed when considering the ages and distances claimed by modern astronomy.

## References

[1] Gass I. Smith P.J. and Wilson R.C.L., *1972 Understanding the Earth* 2nd Ed. Open University Press

[2] Hahn et al. Survey of rate perturbation of nuclear decay. *Radiochemica Acta* 1976 23:23-37

[3] See A. Snelling *'Dating Methods' Origins* (Journal of Biblical Creation Society) *Creation – Basics and Beyond* No. 27, February 2000, pp.32-36

4 Vardiman L. *The age of the earth's atmosphere: a study of helium flux through the atmosphere.* (Institute for Creation Research 1990) p.27

5 Quoted in A. J. Monty White, *Radiocarbon dating*

6 See Gish's article – Chapter 5 in *Creation and Evolution* edited by Derek Burke (IVP 1985)

7 *New Scientist* Vol. 68, p.513

## For further reading

1. Paul D. Ackerman It's a Young World after all (Baker Book House, 1986)

2. A.J. Monty White, *How Old is the Earth?*, (Evangelical Press, 1985).

3. John Woodmarappe *The Mythology of Modern Dating Methods* (Institute for Creation Research, 1999)

4. John D. Morris *The Young Earth* (Master Books, 1994)

5. Paul M. Steidl, *The Earth, the Stars, and the Bible*, (Presbyterian and Reformed, 1979).

6. John Byl *God and Cosmos* (Banner of Truth Trust 2001)

7. Stuart Burgess *He made the Stars also* (Day One Publications, 2001)

# 5.
# The true history of man

**Jim's friend phoned up in a slight panic. 'Look, Jim,' he said, 'I'm supposed to be meeting a Mr Wong at the airport in half an hour and I can't possibly make it. I've been unavoidably held up – do you think you could go for me? I've not met Mr Wong, so I can't tell you what he looks like, but I'm sure you'll have no problem in finding him. Thanks!'**

**Jim set off at once, but could not help feeling rather worried. How would he know Mr Wong when he reached the airport? He tried to work out his approach. With a name like Wong, the man must be Chinese. And if he is called Mr Wong, he cannot be a young boy – he must be a mature man. If he is Chinese he will be dark-haired, yellow-skinned, rather short in stature and with oriental eyes.**

**When Jim reached the airport he hastily scanned the crowd looking for such a figure. Red-haired women, fair children, tall men – all sorts were there, but Jim hardly noticed these in his search for a short, dark Chinese gentleman. After half an hour he had found no one answering that description. Just then the public address system announced that Mr Wong was waiting at a certain exit. Jim hurried towards it – to be confronted with a tall, fair European who introduced himself as Mr Wong. Jim apologized for his friend's absence and his own delay – and realized that his original theory about him had been hopelessly wide of the mark and that it had in fact hampered his search.**

That story illustrates the way in which a scientist works. When he sets out to solve a problem, he cannot possibly consider all the facts that might have some bearing on it, any more than Jim could have asked all the people at the airport if they were Mr Wong. He therefore formulates a theory, just as Jim did, and then sets out to test it.

If all the evidence points to the theory being wrong, the honest thing is for the scientist to abandon that theory and develop a new one that does fit the facts. It would have been most unreasonable for Jim to have clung to his theory that Mr Wong was Chinese when confronted by such clear evidence that he was not.

When the theory of evolution was first put forward, it seemed to some scientists to be a reasonable theory and they therefore set out to test it. The evidence collected over the past 150 years, however, does not support that theory and in fact shows it to be quite unacceptable. On the other hand, the evidence supports what the Bible teaches about the early history of the earth. I am not suggesting that the biblical teaching is simply an alternative theory to evolution, for I believe it to be the truth. I am suggesting that if non-Christian scientists would accept it as an alternative theory, they would find it to be quite in accord with the facts, whereas the theory of evolution is not. I hope in this final chapter to present the biblical account and to show how much better it explains the facts.

The Bible's account of the history of the earth can be divided into four eras:
1. The creation week.
2. The period stretching from the Fall to just before Noah's Flood.
3. The Flood itself.
4. The period from the Flood down to the present day.

We shall examine each in turn.

## 1. The creation week

The Bible tells us that in the beginning God created the heavens and the earth. The earth at that time was covered with water. Then God created light independently of the sun, which had not yet been created.

The account of the second day includes an event that we don't really understand, but which could be important in the early history of the earth. We are told that God created an expanse (or firmament) in the midst of the waters. This separated the waters that were under this expanse from the waters that were above it.

On the third day we are told that God gathered together all the water that was upon the earth into one place and dry land appeared. The clear indication is that there was thus, at first, one ocean on the earth. The implication is that a far smaller proportion of the earth's surface was then under water than is so at present. Also on the third day, God created vegetation and all kinds of seed-bearing plants. Plants were thus created *before* the sun, an idea that is quite incompatible with the theory of evolution.

On the fourth day God created the sun, moon and stars. The fifth saw the creation of many creatures such as birds, butterflies, flying reptiles, bats and sea creatures. On the sixth day God made the land animals and finally mankind. God told Adam that he was allowed to eat the plants for food, man thus being created a vegetarian.

'God saw all that he had made, and it was very good.'

What exactly did God see? We can only make a very inadequate attempt at imagining what that wonderful world was like. Adam and Eve did not need to wear clothes, which implies that the weather was consistently warm. One thing that the Bible tells us is that it did not rain on earth at that time. Nevertheless, there was an abundant supply of water. There were many rivers and it seems that they may have been fed by a subterranean source of water.

Such conditions are ideal for the growth of plants and the land must have been covered with lush vegetation. Trees and flowers must have grown in abundance, especially as at first there was no competition from weeds. Fruit and vegetables would have been readily available to provide food for man and the animals. Consequently, the earth could have supported many kinds of animals in vast numbers. The warm rivers and ocean would have been teeming with fish and water animals.

If that is the picture the Bible draws, what is the evidence for the existence of such conditions on earth?

Firstly, there is much evidence that both vegetation and animal life were more abundant in the past. Coal, oil and natural gas are all present throughout the earth in vast amounts, giving an indication of how much plant life there once was. The huge numbers of fossil animals also speak of a very well-populated earth.

We have already mentioned that God gave mankind permission to feed on fruit and vegetables alone and it is interesting to note that humans still have basically the tooth structure of a herbivore, that is, of a creature that feeds on plants.

What a wonderful world that was! Constant warm temperature, an abundant food supply, no problems from climate, weeds, or infections of any kind. No diseases existed on earth at that time and the bacteria that did exist would all have been helpful to mankind (as, incidentally, most still are.) Death and decay would have been unknown. It was not intended that Adam should die or that he should see death around him. The world that God had made was very good; and in addition to all the material blessings, Adam and Eve enjoyed the close presence of God, who walked and talked with them.

It was therefore utterly unexpected and unreasonable that Adam should throw all this away by sinning against God at the first external temptation. As a result of Adam's disobedience and rebellion, God placed a curse on his wonderful creation.

## 2. From the Fall to the Flood

Adam's fall brought death into the world. People now found that weeds and pests hampered farming, disease impaired health and ageing affected the body. However, it seems that the world immediately after the fall was still a much better place to live in than the one that we have at the moment. This is implied by the fact that people then lived to a great age. The Bible tells us that the average age at death for those who lived between the fall and the Flood was 900 years.

This has sometimes worried Christians, but there is no reason to doubt it. Conditions on earth at that time must have been much more conducive to long life. Moreover, accounts of people once living to a great age are not confined to the Bible. They occur in the folklore and traditions of almost every ancient race. Egypt, Syria, Persia, India and Greece all possess traditions of a long-lived race during a previous age.

We shall consider later possible reasons for the loss of this ability to live to a great age. For the moment it is enough to say that there is historical evidence to support the Bible's account and no scientific reasons for doubting it.

It is tragic that humans, so materially blessed by God, should have incurred his anger by their increasingly sinful and disgusting behaviour. Mankind's rejection of God and of his standards finally warranted a terrible judgement. Only one man was left who feared and served God – Noah. The Lord therefore decreed that Noah and his family should escape the awful events to follow.

## 3. The Flood and its immediate aftermath

How lightly we view the Flood! Yet the events of that year affect us still today. The whole climate of the earth was altered; the volcanic and earthquake activity that persists today began then. Another consequence still affecting us is the dramatic reduction in the length of the human life span to less than one tenth of its original value. Genesis chapter 6 verse 3 makes it plain that this was a deliberate plan of the Lord – to reduce the life span to a maximum of 120 years. He was not prepared to allow people a longer life span in which to defy him and live godless lives. It is interesting that 120 years is now regarded as the natural maximum life span for humans. Occasionally people do reach this age, but virtually never do they live much beyond it.

The Flood, then was the greatest and most significant natural disaster ever to affect the earth. Catastrophe on such a scale will never be repeated until the final judgement. What exactly did happen? The Bible makes several statements about the Flood in Genesis 7 verses 11 and 12. It began very suddenly and dramatically – the precise day is carefully noted. (It would be a full year after this before Noah and his family were able to leave the ark.) Two things seem to have happened simultaneously. 'The underground waters burst forth on the earth' and 'the floodgates of the

heavens were opened.' It seems that the earth's crust was broken apart by terrible volcanic and earthquake activity as a result of which vast amounts of subterranean water poured out onto the land and into the ocean. At the same time, rain fell in torrents from the sky, perhaps having originated from the 'water above the expanse' referred to in Genesis 1. The rain fell torrentially for 40 days and 40 nights. By these means, sufficient water reached the surface of the earth to cover it completely, so that even the highest mountains of those days were submerged to a depth of at least 6.5 metres.

What is the evidence that such a flood actually happened? There is abundant evidence and it comes from several academic disciplines.

Some of the evidence is *historical.* In every part of the world are found traditions speaking of a great flood which once covered the earth and destroyed all but a tiny remnant of the human race. Many of them speak of a great ark which saved some people and animals and finally landed on a mountain.

The evidence on which we concentrate here is *scientific.* Despite the denials of geologists and evolutionists, the findings of geology and palaeontology point unmistakably to great catastrophe. We may summarise the evidence under three main heads.

1. At least three-quarters of the earth's surface, including the tops of most mountains, is covered with sedimentary rock. The sediment must have been eroded from some previous locations, then transported and deposited. This is exactly what happens during a flood. Much evidence shows that these thick layers of sediment were deposited within a very short time, and not gradually over millions of years. Many fossil animals and tree trunks, for example, are to be found extending through several strata often six metres or more in thickness. The top parts of these 'polystrate' fossils are as well preserved as the lower, showing that the whole animal or tree was submerged in a short time by rapidly deposited layers of sediment. In some parts of the United States huge reptiles are found buried in this fashion. If the sedimentation had been at present rates, it would have taken 5000 years for these animals to be covered. Near Edinburgh a fossilised tree trunk was found. It was about 24 metres long and intersected ten or twelve different beds; from its uniform fossilisation it was obvious that it had been buried rapidly.

2. The study of coal provides evidence of flood conditions. Many facts suggest that the coal seams were formed when vegetation was uprooted and redeposited by flood waters, rather than accumulating slowly in a peat bog as many evolutionists believe. For example, upright tree trunks more than three metres in height have been found in coal

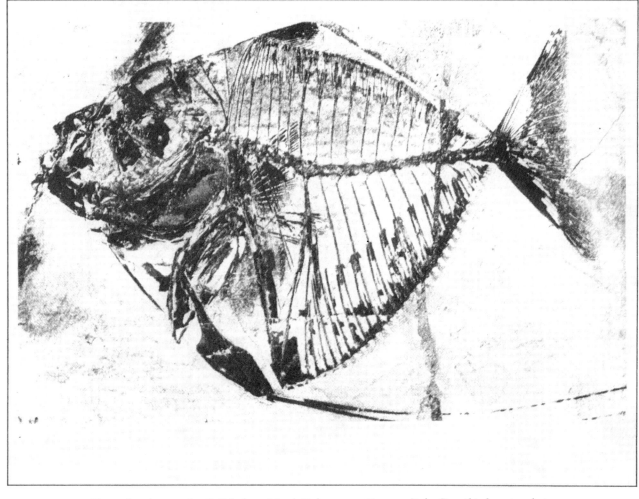

*Mene rhombea; a fossil fish from Monk Bolea, near Verona, Italy. Two thirds natural size.*

beds. Some trees are positioned with their tops downward in the coal and so could not have grown in place. Marine fossils have been found embedded in coal. So too have boulders of rock that could only have come from a considerable distance away.

3. The fossil record is of special importance when considering evidence for the Flood. For nearly two hundred years an intense debate has raged as to how the fossils should be interpreted. The picture is complex and creationists are continually seeking to improve their understanding of the data. That the fossil record speaks of catastrophe is undeniable and it is interesting that the pendulum amongst evolutionists is swinging back in the direction of admitting this and including catastrophe in their thinking. Incredibly vast numbers of fossils exist and flood conditions are ideal for producing them, since a

creature must be rapidly buried in sediment if it is to fossilise rather than decay or be eaten by scavengers. The wiping out of the dinosaurs and the many fossilised shoals of fish that obviously died suddenly are all factors pointing to a terrible catastrophe such as the Flood would have been.

However, not all of the fossil evidence depicts a catastrophic scenario. For example, in the rocks are sometimes to be found hundreds of well-preserved dinosaur footprints, showing that the dinosaurs were ambling along in a normal kind of way in a gentle environment. (In other cases, the indications suggest a more unstable environment.) Dinasaur nests have been found neatly arranged, showing that something approaching normal life was going on. Most creationists would agree that some of the fossils date from the post-flood era, when the earth was adjusting to new conditions and becoming

repopulated by both animal and human life. It may have taken some hundreds of years for this to happen and during that time conditions may well have been more unstable than they are today, producing more flooding on a localized scale. This is possibly hinted at in the promise that the Lord gave to Noah that he would never again flood the whole earth, giving the rainbow as a guarantee of that promise. Perhaps Noah and his descendants needed that reassurance because of the unstable conditions immediately after the Flood.

There is a general order to the fossils in the rocks. Marine invertebrates are found in the lowest levels and constitute the vast majority of fossils. Then, working upwards, we find fish, amphibians, reptiles, mammals and human remains. Evolutionists regard this sequence as a record of the evolution of life, although they themselves are aware of many problems with that view. However, it could equally well reflect the order in which the earth was repopulated after the Flood. Some humility is in order in both the creationist and the evolutionist camps as we struggle towards a correct interpretation of the amazing fossil record.

No-one could hope to escape the terrible catastrophe of the Flood unless God protected him, and before long every person on the face of the earth was dead except Noah and his family. God then caused the floodwaters to abate. It is possible that mountains were thrust up and that ocean floors sank down to accommodate the vast amount of water. Eventually all was ready for Noah to step out of the ark and begin a new life.

## 4. From the Flood to the present day.

What a different world confronted Noah! Gone was the wonderful environment that he had formerly known. A much more frightening and unstable situation now prevailed. It must soon have become obvious that the life span was decreasing. It is possible that the changes brought about by the Flood led to an increase in cosmic radiation reaching the earth and therefore to an increased rate of mutation of the genetic material in the body cells of Noah and his family. This effect would have accumulated over succeeding generations, and together with the generally harder way of life would have ensured a steady decline in the human life span. Over a number of generations this decline continued until a new life span was reached, now less than one tenth of its span before the Flood.

God knew that it would be much more difficult for people to survive on this new type of earth. In particular, food would be harder to come by. The Lord therefore told Noah that from now on people would be permitted to eat meat as well as vegetables and fruit.

The terrible judgement of the Flood, earned by the sins of mankind and for which there is so much evidence, affects us still today. Many species of animals and plants have become extinct. Food is no longer easy to find. Volcanoes and earthquakes occur. Climate is often inhospitable and can even provide dangers. Our life span has been radically reduced. All this because of sin.

In these five studies, I have sought to show that the scientific evidence fully supports the Bible and disproves the theory of evolution. How is it then that the majority of scientists still hold to the theory and even mock those who believe that the Bible is true? Why are they so convinced of their theory if it is false and contradicted by the evidence? It is important to realise that no scientist operates from a neutral or objective philosophical position. The prevailing philosophy amongst most scientists today is 'naturalism' which assumes that the supernatural does not exist or at least that it has no relevance to them as scientists. That assumption will affect the way that they view and interpret the data. The Lord himself has given us a clear indication of how he views the situation that prevails today. Indeed, he has warned us to expect it. In the following passage of Scripture, he has warned us of the fearful end, both of those who deny him and of ungodly theories themselves.

'First of all, you must understand that in the last days scoffers will come, scoffing and following their own evil desires. They will say, "Where is this 'coming' he promised? Ever since our fathers died, everything goes on as it has since the beginning of creation." But they deliberately forget that long ago by God's word the heavens existed and the earth was formed out of water and by water. By these waters also the world of that time was deluged and destroyed. By the same word the present heavens and earth are reserved for fire, being kept for the day of judgement and destruction of ungodly men... But the day of the Lord will come like a thief. The heavens will disappear with a roar; the elements will be destroyed by fire, and the earth and everything in it will be laid bare... Therefore, dear friends, since you already know this, be on your guard so that you may not be carried away by the error of lawless men and fall from your secure position. But grow in the grace and knowledge of our Lord and Saviour Jesus Christ. To him be glory both now and for ever! Amen'

(2 Peter 3).

34